Say the sounds and blend them together to read the word. Where is the dog in the picture?

dog

Look at the letters and say the sounds. See how quickly you can say all of them.

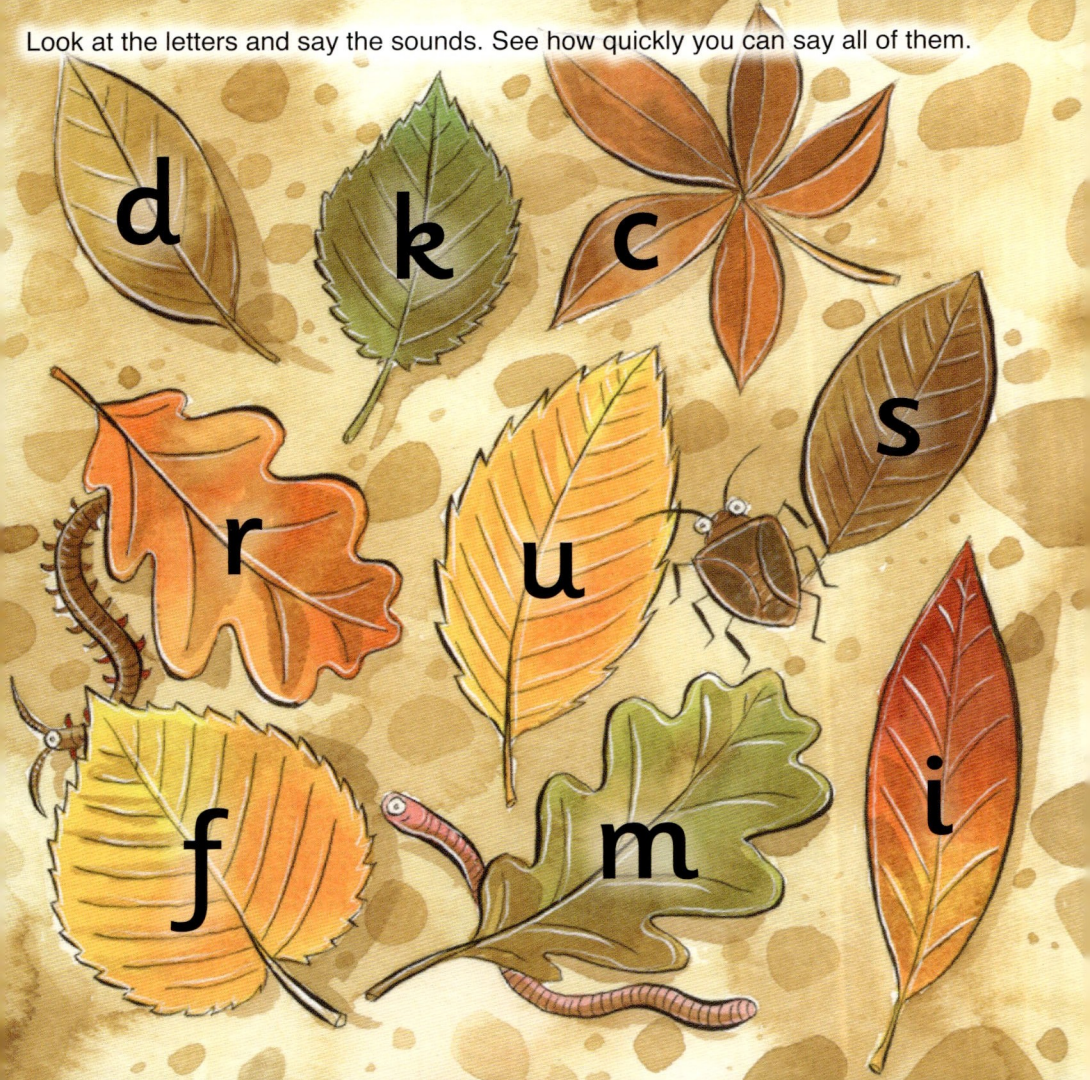

dug

mud

pot

sun

socks

bat

rag

Say the word *slug* and listen out for the sounds: *slug* – /s-l-u-g/.
(There is one sound dot underneath the slug for each sound in the word.)

red

a black dog

robin

pumpkin